Positively Me!

A Self-esteem Project for Teachers and Pupils

Lesley K. Petersen

Brilliant Publications

Publisher's Information

Brilliant Publications
www.brilliantpublications.co.uk

Sales
BEBC (Brilliant Publications)
Albion Close, Parkstone, Poole, Dorset, BH12 3LL, UK
Tel: 01202 712910   Fax: 0845 1309300

Editorial
Unit 10, Sparrow Hall Farm, Edlesborough,
Dunstable, Bedfordshire, LU6 2ES, UK

The name Brilliant Publications and its logo are registered trade marks.

Published in the UK by Brilliant Publications.

Printed in England

ISBN 978-1-903853-13-9

10 9 8 7 6 5 4 3 2 1

If you would like further information about any of our other titles or to request a catalogue, please visit our website www.brilliantpublications.co.uk or telephone 01525 222292.

Contents

Introduction

Self-esteem is a concept that many people struggle to understand, especially in relation to themselves – their sense of worth and well-being and how these influence their interactions and relationships with others.

The self-esteem project outlined in this resource is designed to assist you, the teacher, to help your pupils to understand what self-esteem is, and to identify their own self-esteem and what influences it. Integral to this learning is the natural influence of a person's self-esteem on relationships with others, such as family, friends and teachers.

This resource comprises several sections, each offering a particular theme relating to self-esteem and incorporating photocopiable sheets for pupil activities. These activities and exercises provide you and your pupils with a broad range of self-esteem scenarios. More specifically, they encourage pupils to explore and examine their lifestyles, the decisions they make, the language they use and much more.

This book fits in well with the National Curriculum's non-statutory guidelines for PSHE and Citizenship, and each activity is referenced to the National Curriculum Programme of Study for this area.

An On-going Approach to Self-esteem

The National Curriculum states:

'During Key Stage 2, pupils learn about themselves as growing and changing individuals with their own experiences and ideas, and as members of their communities. They become mature, independent and self-confident. They learn how to make more confident and informed choices about their health and environment; to take more responsibility, individually and as a group, for their own learning; and to resist bullying.'

At Key Stage 2 the National Curriculum suggests that children should be:

★ Developing confidence and responsibility, making the most of their abilities
★ Preparing to play an active role as citizens
★ Developing a healthy, safer lifestyle
★ Developing good relationships and respecting the differences between people

This book focuses on self-esteem, teaching what it is and how to improve it. Its aim is to give children a better sense of self and increase their confidence.

Pupils are encouraged to read and complete the handout on 'Setting Goals' (pages 65–68) as a starting point for the project. This can be an individual activity, with opportunity for whole-class discussion of the significance of setting goals, both short- and long-term. The project ends with a self-evaluation questionnaire ('Checking my Goal Achievement', pages 72–73), and an activity aimed at helping pupils identify long-term goals (pages 69–71); you may wish to collect the latter after the pupils have completed it and then provide feedback on an individual basis. Also encourage pupils to keep a 'journal' in which they can collect information and material throughout the project that has meaning for them and is useful for the future.

However, before you embark on the self-esteem project with the pupils, I suggest that you consider your own self-esteem by reading section 1 on pages 6–8 of this book and completing the activities that it contains. If we, as teachers, wish to help other people learn about and develop healthy, positive self-esteem, we must first of all learn about and develop our own.

Self-esteem is a natural, on-going factor in our lives. This project is also on-going in its use and purpose for pupils and teachers alike.

Lesley K. Petersen

1 General Strategies Related to Teaching the Self-esteem Project

Your Own Self-esteem

One of the key considerations for people concerned with encouraging others to achieve healthy self-esteem is the 'healthiness' of their own self-concept and self-acceptance. To help pupils to develop healthy self-esteem, it is important that you possess a healthy attitude towards yourself. Self-acceptance and self-understanding are vital requirements of the teacher, especially when working with pupils to encourage the same.

So, before continuing with this resource, go to the 'Self-esteem Checklist' on page 8 and take some time to work through it. Your familiarity with this activity and others in this book will help you to guide your pupils through the project and focus your expectations for their learning.

Developing Pupils' Self-esteem

You can incorporate strategies to help pupils develop healthy self-esteem into your everyday lesson planning and teaching by applying general principles such as use of language, constructive feedback, praising pupils, etc. You probably already use various strategies to develop your pupils' self-esteem. Jot them down here, and also list any other strategies that you might use. When you have done this, compare your list with the one on the next page. Think about how you can incorporate the strategies it contains and your own ideas into your lesson plans, either as one-off sessions, a series of lessons or as part of the usual class project.

Strategies I Use to Encourage Pupils' Self-esteem

Self-esteem Builders

The following list of ideas is for you to use with your pupils at any time, whether in a formal teaching session or whenever you are in contact with them, such as during break-time, or when passing pupils in the corridor. Whatever the situation, these self-esteem builders are useful, powerful tools:

★ Always try to use the pupils' names.

★ Have conversations with pupils at unplanned times.

★ Show interest in pupils' lives both within and outside school (in their families, hobbies and activities).

★ Provide opportunities for pupils to display their work in the school environment.

★ Openly celebrate pupils' successes.

★ Enable pupils to work together co-operatively.

★ Avoid criticizing – provide constructive feedback.

★ Avoid making assumptions about pupils' behaviour.

★ Provide opportunities for pupils to problem-solve in a safe environment (eg. the learning environment that you establish within this self-esteem project).

★ Provide opportunities for pupils to make their own decisions about certain aspects of the class environment or lesson structure.

★ Highlight mistakes as learning experiences.

★ Allocate responsibilities for certain/all pupils; encourage self-responsibility.

★ Consider individual learning styles so your presentation and learning materials meet the different needs.

★ Allow opportunities for celebrating pupils' successes – display their work, praise them, invite them to share their ideas with the rest of the class.

★ Incorporate goal-setting activities in all curriculum areas. Ask the pupil to write down their goals in their journals and encourage them to review these regularly (as part of the self-esteem project and in their own time).

★ Create challenges in their learning – it is not just about textbook information but how they relate to other people, their social skills and learning about themselves.

★ Help pupils to identify their strengths and areas for improvement – this does not just have to be in the 'academic' sense.

★ Start each day/lesson with a warm-up activity, to establish the mood and introduce the topic.

★ Discover the things your pupils value – about school, or their personal values.

★ Build a session around this subject.

Self-esteem Checklist

Read through the following statements and indicate with a tick (✔) how you feel about each one with regards to yourself. Each statement will provide you with an idea of the sorts of things you need to be aware of to gauge the health of your self-esteem.

		Always true	Sometimes true	Seldom/ never true
1.	I feel confident setting goals and achieving them.	❏	❏	❏
2.	I find it easy to ask for help when I need to.	❏	❏	❏
3.	I do not feel the need to compete with my peers.	❏	❏	❏
4.	I believe I learn from my mistakes. It does not mean I am failing.	❏	❏	❏
5.	I seldom get upset when another person criticizes me.	❏	❏	❏
6.	I don't often worry about what might happen.	❏	❏	❏
7.	I am able to express how I feel.	❏	❏	❏
8.	I do not feel that I would rather be someone else.	❏	❏	❏
9.	I am able to cope well with my work.	❏	❏	❏
10.	If I do not understand something, I will ask.	❏	❏	❏
11.	I rarely dwell on negative things.	❏	❏	❏
12.	I feel in control of situations and events in my life.	❏	❏	❏
13.	I find it easy to genuinely compliment other people.	❏	❏	❏
14.	I accept compliments easily.	❏	❏	❏
15.	I have friends who support me.	❏	❏	❏
16.	I am confident that I can deal with most situations.	❏	❏	❏
17.	I accept that I have choices.	❏	❏	❏
18.	I can identify my strengths and areas I need to work on.	❏	❏	❏
19.	I don't feel anyone else is better than I am.	❏	❏	❏
20.	I feel good about myself.	❏	❏	❏

Understanding Self-esteem

In this section, pupils will explore the meaning of self-esteem, complete a checklist to identify their own level of self-esteem, gain an understanding of the differences between healthy and unhealthy self-esteem and work through some activities to help them to identify their own 'healthiness'.

It is important that pupils complete this whole area of learning (ie identifying what self-esteem is) before advancing to the other sections of this project which deal with how to create and maintain a positive, healthy self-esteem.

What is self-esteem?

Many words and phrases can be used to describe self-esteem. It is important for pupils to associate definitions so that the concept of self-esteem is clear and relevant to them. When someone says, 'I have good self-esteem,' one often wonders what that actually means – what, for example, is 'good'?

The pupils' 'Self-esteem Checklist' (pages 16–17) enables them to collect data about themselves as a starting point for learning more about the topic of self-esteem. If they do not understand this concept and how it relates to them, there will be no context for their learning. Completing the checklist not only helps them gain an understanding of the concept but also clarifies for them the terminology that you will be using. The checklist is personal to each pupil, but you could follow it up by creating a class 'round robin', asking pupils to share at least one answer. This would allow you to gain some appreciation of your pupils' level of comprehension of the topic as well as some insight into how they see themselves.

So, let us look more closely at what is meant by self-esteem. The list below provides some common definitions of this term and can also be used with the pupils. (See in particular *Pupil Activities 3 and 4*, pages 12–13.)

Self-esteem is:
- ★   The way you see and think about yourself.
- ★   Recognizing your positive attributes and strengths.
- ★   Acknowledging that you are a worthy person.
- ★   Maintaining a positive, realistic self-image.
- ★   Respecting yourself – who you are, what you have to offer others.
- ★   Eliminating the negative self-critic ('self-talk').
- ★   Identifying and recognizing your own needs.
- ★   Maintaining healthy, positive 'self-talk'.
- ★   Living by your own values and beliefs.
- ★   Believing in yourself, and accepting who you are.
- ★   Understanding yourself.
- ★   You can change your self-esteem by changing the way you think about yourself.
- ★   *Compassion* for yourself is the core of self-esteem.

Self-esteem is NOT:
- ★   The way other people see or describe you.

Positive self-esteem is visible in people who take care of themselves physically and emotionally, who respond appropriately to other people and who do not build themselves up by putting other people down. Positive self-esteem helps people to enjoy life as much as possible. It is an unknown quantity, and certainly it is different for each person.

We are all capable of developing, maintaining and building our self-esteem, and of changing aspects of ourselves, and consequently our lives, if we decide we want or need to. What matters is that this decision is our own. So many people are eager to offer uninvited feedback about how we look or present ourselves, how we talk, whether we did a good job, whether we completed a task well or whether we should improve. Positive self-esteem does not grow out of this sort of input from other people; it grows from the individual.

Therefore, the starting point for developing positive self-esteem is acceptance of oneself, before attempting to build, change or improve upon it. That is the key focus of this section – helping pupils to identify their self-esteem as it is now, before venturing through the other sections that focus more on different strategies to develop or improve self-esteem.

The aim here is to help pupils individually, and at times collectively, to identify, recognize and acknowledge their own level of self-esteem and their satisfaction with this, as determined by them, and not someone else.

 **Pupil Activity**

> ## The Self-esteem Tree
> **National Curriculum:** 1a
> **Time:** 15–20 minutes
> **You will need:** Board, board pens, one copy of 'The Self-esteem Tree' (page 11) per pupil
> **Organization:** Whole-class introduction and individual work

1. As an introduction to this section, ask the pupils to brainstorm what they think self-esteem means. A fun approach is to draw a large tree on the board (see page 11), with the branches of the tree representing the different definitions of self-esteem, and the roots of the tree indicating where self-esteem starts.

2. Provide pupils with the handout of the tree (page 11), so that they can fill in the words and phrases to create their own 'Self-esteem Tree'.

The Self-esteem Tree

What is self-esteem? Use the tree to brainstorm some of your ideas.

Why is a tree a good object for representing self-esteem?

The branches define self-esteem

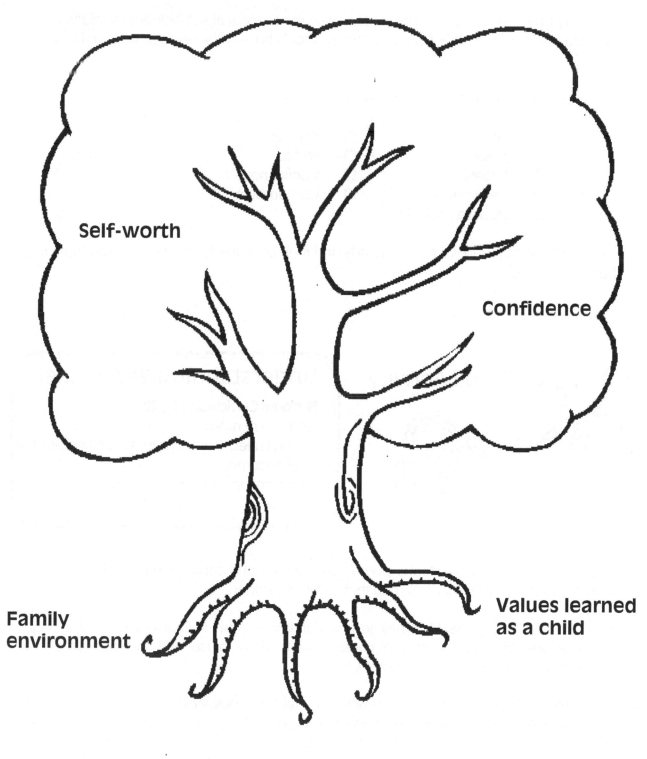

Self-worth

Confidence

Family environment

Values learned as a child

The roots of self-esteem

Pupil Activity 2

Understanding Self-esteem

National Curriculum: 1a
Time: 30 minutes
You will need: Board, board pens, pupils' journals
Organization: Whole-class introduction and individual work

1. Help the pupils to make some connections with the concept of self-esteem by relating this term to other, more familiar words that probably have a clearer meaning for them. The following words/phrases may help them in this regard. Write them on the board and ask your pupils to work together as a whole class to discuss the meaning of each word/phrase. Write their ideas beside each one.

   ❏ Worth
   ❏ Value
   ❏ Beliefs
   ❏ Self-image
   ❏ Positive attributes

   ❏ Self-talk
   ❏ Needs
   ❏ Confidence
   ❏ Compassion

2. Encourage the pupils to write these words and their collective idea for describing them in their own journals.

Pupil Activity 3

Understanding Self-esteem

National Curriculum: 1a, 1b
Time: 20 minutes
You will need: Key terms from *Pupil Activity 2* pupils' journals
Organization: Pair work and written feedback

1. Select one or two of the key terms (from *Pupil Activity 2*) and encourage each pupil to think of a time when they felt this way, and then tell their partner.

2. Now ask them to express what they have said in written form, in their journals, using only one sentence. Write up the sentence construction for them to use, and give an example of a complete sentence to help them get started.
   Example:
   Teacher (states): 'Think of a time when you felt/feel **confident**.'
   Pupils (writes in journal): 'I feel **confident** when I ... '

The Self-esteem Mind-map

National Curriculum: 1a, 1b
Time: 20 minutes
You will need: One copy of 'Self-esteem Mind-map' (page 14) per pupil
Organization: Individual work

Pupil Activity

1. Provide pupils with the mind-map of self-esteem key words (page 14) and ask them to complete it by creating their own definitions, using personal experiences. Below is an example of how this map might look when completed.

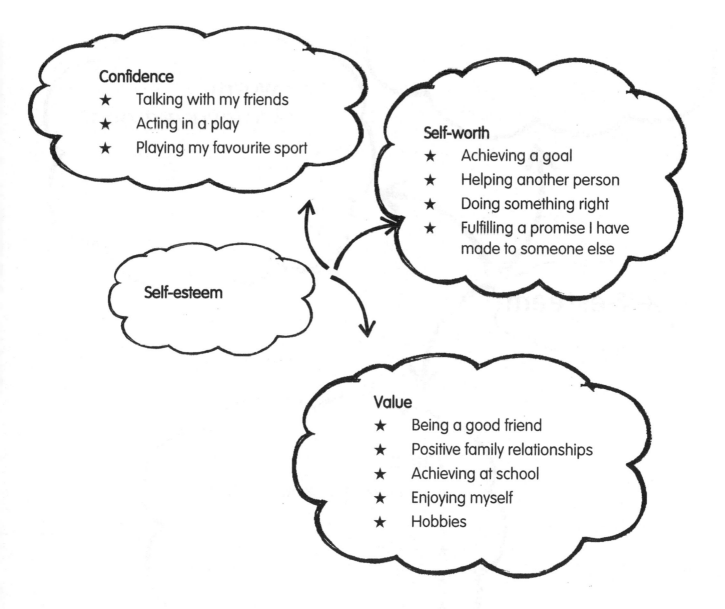

Confidence
★ Talking with my friends
★ Acting in a play
★ Playing my favourite sport

Self-worth
★ Achieving a goal
★ Helping another person
★ Doing something right
★ Fulfilling a promise I have made to someone else

Self-esteem

Value
★ Being a good friend
★ Positive family relationships
★ Achieving at school
★ Enjoying myself
★ Hobbies

Self-esteem Mind-map

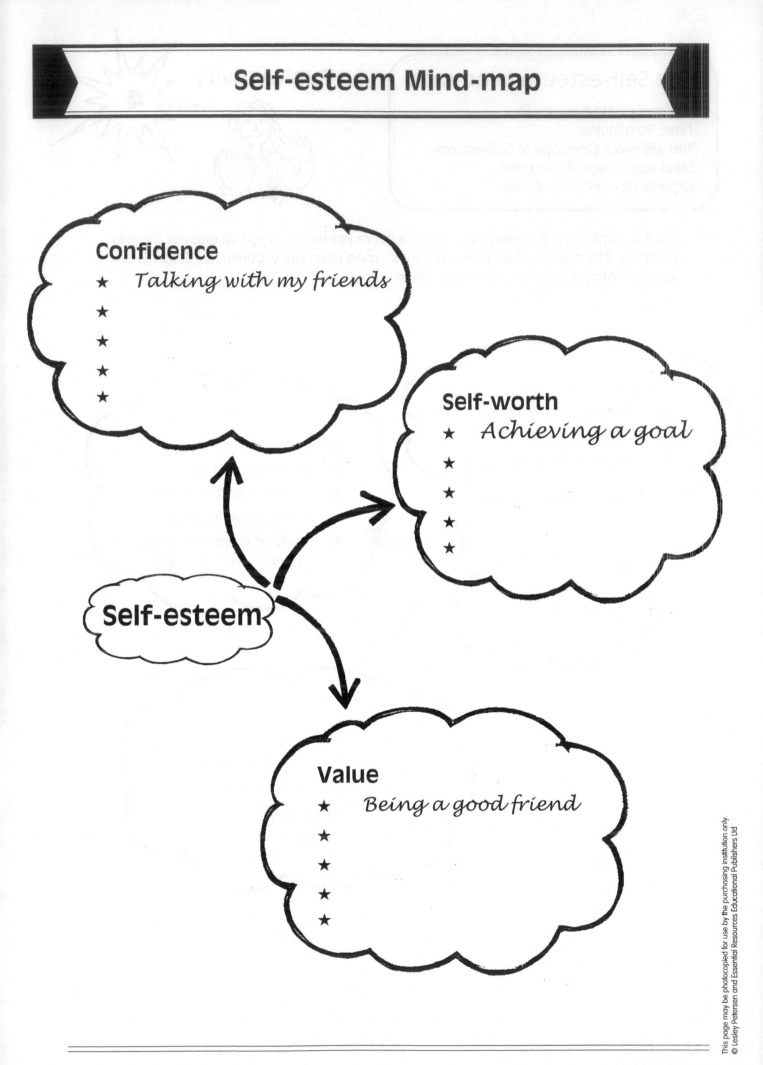

Confidence
★ *Talking with my friends*
★
★
★
★

Self-worth
★ *Achieving a goal*
★
★
★
★

Self-esteem

Value
★ *Being a good friend*
★
★
★
★

Self-assessment ('Who am I?')

It can be very easy for children, and adults, to create an image of themselves based on what other people tell them, what they observe as acceptable in society (eg. slim and beautiful women are successful) and what different messages (whether overt or covert) they receive from adults and other significant figures.

However, what is more important is how we see ourselves – the messages we give ourselves ('self-talk'), and other people's descriptions that we choose to either accept or reject, deciding whether these fit our own self-concept.

Some of us need a bit of help to develop a realistic 'I'm OK' picture of ourselves. If we have experienced mostly negative feedback from others, then it is very likely that we will have developed a negative image of ourselves, which can be extremely difficult to change (this is addressed in 'The Power of Self-talk' section, pages 35–48).

Self-assessment
National Curriculum: 1a, 1b
Time: 30 minutes
You will need: One copy of 'Self-esteem Checklist' (page 16–17) per pupil
Organization: Individual work and feedback in pairs

Pupil Activity 5

1. Hand out the 'Self-esteem Checklist' (pages 16–17) for the pupils to complete, initially on their own.

2. Direct the pupils to read through the questions and to decide how true each statement is for them.

3. When everyone has finished, ask the pupils to pair up and discuss their answers together.

Self-esteem Checklist

(This is an evaluation, not a test.)

Score as follows:
    0 = never true
    1 = sometimes true
    2 = most of the time true
    3 = all of the time true

Read through each statement and circle the number that best describes your response. This checklist is just an evaluation of how you measure your level of self-esteem at present. Answer each statement based on what you believe about yourself, not what you think you should be doing, saying or feeling.

1.   I set and achieve my own goals.

        0   1   2   3

2.   I am open to new ideas and welcome suggestions from others.

        0   1   2   3

3.   I celebrate my successes.

        0   1   2   3

4.   I recognize my strengths and areas for improvement.

        0   1   2   3

5.   I do not feel a failure when I make a mistake.

        0   1   2   3

6.   I believe we learn from our mistakes.

        0   1   2   3

7.   I remain open-minded when presented with a problem.

        0   1   2   3

8.   I do not blame other people for my mistakes or setbacks.

        0   1   2   3

9.   I am able to maintain a positive attitude.

        0   1   2   3

10.   I do not give up easily when something is important to me.

        0   1   2   3

(This is an evaluation, not a test.)

11. I do not believe that putting other people down makes me better or stronger.

        0   1   2   3

12. I do not need to compete with others or compare my skills and achievements with theirs.

        0   1   2   3

13. I am motivated to achieve any goal I set myself.

        0   1   2   3

14. I do not have a need for people to pay attention to me.

        0   1   2   3

15. I like to take care of myself physically, mentally and emotionally.

        0   1   2   3

16. I anticipate and enjoy change.

        0   1   2   3

17. I happily seek advice or help when I need to.

        0   1   2   3

18. I view criticism as feedback for improvement or change.

        0   1   2   3

19. I am comfortable with my own company.

        0   1   2   3

20. I readily voice my opinions.

        0   1   2   3

21. I do not feel the need to please others.

        0   1   2   3

22. I do not need praise from others to feel good about myself or my achievements.

        0   1   2   3

23. I can accept compliments without feeling uncomfortable.

        0   1   2   3

Pupil Activity 6

Recognizing My Personal Qualities

National Curriculum: 1a, 1b
Time: 30 minutes
You will need: One copy of 'Recognizing My Personal Qualities' (page 19) per pupil, board, board pen
Organization: Individual work and class feedback

This activity may be completed as a follow-on from *Pupil Activity 5* or you may choose to use it instead of the 'Self-esteem Checklist' (pages 16–17).

1. Hand out 'Recognizing My Personal Qualities' (page 19) and ask the pupils to complete it. Tell them that they need to read through the instructions at the top of the page, then tick, highlight or circle each quality they believe describes them. Suggest to the pupils that they think of any other qualities they have that are not included on the list and add them in at the bottom of the sheet.

2. Once everyone has finished, use the board to create a mural of words and phrases that describe the pupils, by asking each pupil to offer at least two qualities they have identified.

3. Reinforce the purpose of the activity – that this sort of task helps pupils to realize the positive things about themselves and how much this regular recognition builds positive self-esteem.

Pupil Activity 7

Self-esteem is ...

National Curriculum: 1a, 1b
Time: 10–15 minutes
You will need: One copy of 'Self-esteem is ... ' (page 20) and/or 'Strategies for Building Self-esteem' (page 21) per pupil or per group
Organization: These are extra activities designed for group discussion or individual work

1. Ask the pupils to read through the handouts either in groups or alone.

2. Discuss as a class the key points arising from them.

Recognizing My Personal Qualities

- Circle 10 (or more) of your strongest positive qualities, or write in your own at the bottom.
- Post this page in a prominent place where you live.
- Begin each day by reading your list and affirming all of your positive qualities.

Able	Eager	Ingenious	Progressive
Accepting	Easy-going	Intelligent	Punctual
Accurate	Efficient	Inventive	Quiet
Adaptable	Empathic	Kind	Rational
Adventurous	Energetic	Learning	Realistic
Affectionate	Enterprising	Leisurely	Reasonable
Alert	Enthusiastic	Light-hearted	Reflective
Ambitious	Fair-minded	Likeable	Relaxed
Artistic	Faithful	Logical	Reliable
Assertive	Fit	Lovable	Resourceful
Attractive	Flexible	Loving	Responsible
Bold	Forgiving	Mature	Self-controlled
Calm	Free	Methodical	Sensible
Careful	Friendly	Meticulous	Sincere
Caring	Fulfilled	Mild	Sociable
Cautious	Funny	Moderate	Special
Charming	Generous	Modest	Spontaneous
Cheerful	Gentle	Natural	Stable
Childlike	Glad	Neat	Strong
Clear-thinking	Good-natured	Non-judgmental	Tactful
Clever	Growing	Open-minded	Talented
Compassionate	Happy	Optimistic	Thankful
Competent	Healthy	Organized	Thorough
Confident	Helpful	Original	Tolerant
Conscientious	Honest	Outgoing	Trusting
Considerate	Hopeful	Patient	Trustworthy
Co-operative	Humorous	Peaceful	Understanding
Courageous	Idealistic	Persevering	Uninhibited
Creative	Imaginative	Persistent	Unique
Curious	Impartial	Pleasant	Versatile
Dedicated	Independent	Polite	Warm
Dependable	Individualistic	Positive	Whole
Determined	Industrious	Practical	Witty
Dynamic	Informal	Precise	Zany

Add your own words here:

Self-esteem is ...

★ Self-esteem is the way you see and think about yourself.

★ Self-esteem is not the way other people see you or describe you.

★ Self-esteem is recognizing your positive attributes and strengths.

★ Self-esteem is acknowledging that you are a worthy person.

★ Self-esteem is maintaining a positive, realistic self-image.

★ Self-esteem is respecting yourself – who you are, and what you have to offer others.

★ Self-esteem is recognizing your positive qualities.

★ Self-esteem is eliminating the negative self-critic ('self-talk').

★ Self-esteem is identifying and recognizing your own needs.

★ Self-esteem is maintaining healthy, positive 'self-talk'.

★ Self-esteem is living by your own values and beliefs.

★ Self-esteem is believing in yourself.

★ Self-esteem is respecting yourself.

★ Self-esteem is accepting who you are.

★ Self-esteem is understanding yourself.

★ You can change your self-esteem by changing the way you think about yourself.

★ Compassion for yourself is the core of self-esteem.

Strategies for Building Self-esteem

The following is a list showing how you can improve your self-esteem:

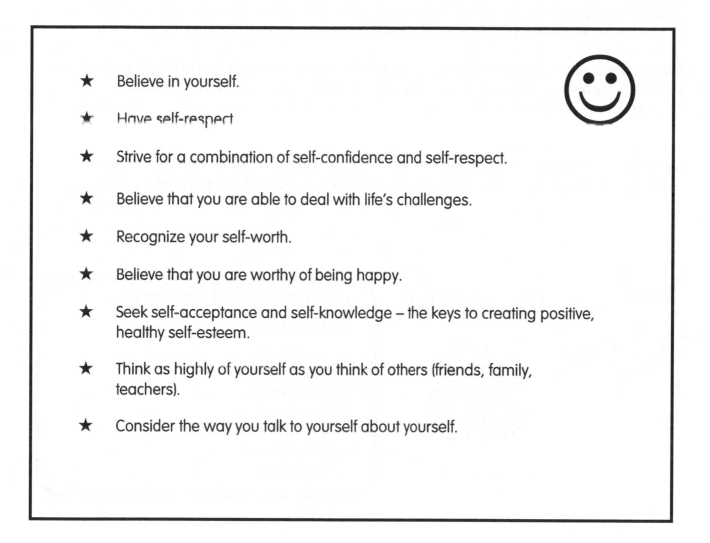

★ Believe in yourself.

★ Have self-respect

★ Strive for a combination of self-confidence and self-respect.

★ Believe that you are able to deal with life's challenges.

★ Recognize your self-worth.

★ Believe that you are worthy of being happy.

★ Seek self-acceptance and self-knowledge – the keys to creating positive, healthy self-esteem.

★ Think as highly of yourself as you think of others (friends, family, teachers).

★ Consider the way you talk to yourself about yourself.

Healthy and Unhealthy Self-esteem
(Recognizing the Difference)

The use of the words 'healthy' and 'unhealthy' in relation to self-esteem provides a more meaningful concept than 'high' and 'low' self-esteem. But how can we tell the difference between what is healthy and what is not? It is important that pupils learn and understand this distinction *before* they try to determine how they can build and maintain their self-esteem.

A teacher once commented that if a pupil was very involved in sporting activities at school, he or she obviously had healthy self-esteem. As you look at the definitions for healthy self-esteem, it should become apparent that being active in sports does not necessarily mean that a pupil is happy and confident in other areas of his or her life. Healthy self-esteem encompasses a person's whole lifestyle, not just certain aspects. As teachers, it is vital not to assume that a pupil is content and happy with himself or herself from one observable factor alone, which is a common mistake. As you work through the activity below, you will need to bear this in mind.

8

Pupil Activity

Healthy and Unhealthy Self-esteem
National Curriculum: 1a, 1b, 4a
Time: 30 minutes
You will need: One copy of 'Healthy and Unhealthy Self-esteem Indicators' (page 23) per pupil, board, board pens
Organization: Class introduction and individual work

This activity leads on well to the next topic, which looks at the causes of unhealthy self-esteem.

1.   Provide the pupils with 'Healthy and Unhealthy Self-esteem Indicators' (page 23).

2.   As a class, brainstorm what is healthy and what is unhealthy, and ask the pupils to write the ideas on the handout as you write them on the board.

3.   When both columns have a list of definitions, ask the pupils to work individually, reading through their own lists and highlighting/circling the words and phrases that they relate strongly to.

Healthy and Unhealthy Self-esteem Indicators

Fill in the boxes with what you think are healthy/unhealthy self-esteem indicators.

Healthy Self-esteem Indicators	Unhealthy Self-esteem Indicators
Example: *Positive interactions with other people*	Example: *No interest in maintaining personal hygiene*

What Causes Unhealthy Self-esteem?
(Perpetuating the 'Lows')

As important as it is to focus on the aspects and behaviour that constitute healthy self-esteem (the main aim and purpose of this resource book), it is also vital that pupils learn to recognize which of their actions and attitudes encourage unhealthy self-esteem – in relation to themselves and to other people. This knowledge will help pupils realize what and how they can change to ensure that they engage in and focus on healthy self-esteem activities.

9 Pupil Activity

> ## Causes of Unhealthy Self-esteem
> **National Curriculum:** 1a, 1b, 4a
> **Time:** 15 minutes
> **You will need:** Board, board pens
> **Organization:** Class discussion

1. Brainstorm pupils' ideas about what constitutes unhealthy self-esteem on the board.

2. Use these ideas as a guideline for a class discussion. Make sure pupils are clear that while the discussion focuses on ways people develop unhealthy self-esteem, a comparison is being made between healthy and unhealthy.

What We Do to Ourselves That Encourages Unhealthy Self-esteem

Prompts
- Putting ourselves down
- Negative 'self-talk'
- Holding onto a rigid idea that 'I should do this/that'
- Ignoring what we value in life
- Accepting 'labels' that other people give us

What We Do to Other People

Prompts
- Blaming others
- Negatively judging their value systems if they are not the same as our own
- Labelling them based on our beliefs
- Calling them names
- Listening to the negative comments of others (about other people)

Causes of Unhealthy Self-esteem

National Curriculum: 1a, 1b, 4a
Time: 10 minutes
You will need: Pupils' journals, headings from *Pupil Activity 9*
Organization: Individual work with class feedback

1. Follow on from *Pupil Activity 9* by guiding pupils to write these ideas in their journals, using the same headings.

2. When your pupils have done this, ask them to highlight the points that relate most strongly to them as individuals – what they do to themselves to perpetuate unhealthy self-esteem and what they do to others that influences those people's unhealthy self-esteem.

3. Remind pupils at the end of the activity that the other lessons in this project focus on how to build and maintain healthy self-esteem.

The Importance of Self-responsibility

Everyone has choices. Some people find this a difficult concept to understand and accept, especially if they are experiencing high levels of stress because they feel that events are 'out of their control'. Children and young adults need guidance to realize that they too can choose what happens in their lives.

By encouraging self-responsibility, you allow the pupils to learn how they influence their own successes, their own sense of satisfaction and achievement of goals, and the outcomes of their actions. This section of material may be useful as a session you plan with them, getting them to identify what self-responsibility means. For now, approach this topic from the perspective of how you, as the teacher, encourage self-responsibility in pupils.

Your Definition of Self-responsibility

_____

_____

_____

This area of learning also helps define your role in the learning process and assists with creating positive, healthy interactions between you and your pupils. Part of the task is helping pupils gain a balanced perspective of what they experience and how much of what happens to them and how they react to it is influenced by the decisions and choices they make.

A good example is when we make a mistake. We often find it all too easy to view this as failing, to see ourselves as a failure. We may blame it on other people/other circumstances, implying that what has happened is not within our control. What we need to remember is that everyone makes mistakes. They are a natural part of life, of learning; we need to see them as opportunities for learning, not recipes for failure. In short, we need to acknowledge that we do make mistakes and that more often than not it is acceptable to do so.

How can you encourage self-responsibility in your pupils? Jot down some ideas now and use this list at any time during the rest of the lessons.

★ _____

★ _____

★ _____

★ _____

★ _____

★ _____

★ _____

Pupil Activity

11

Learning from Your Mistakes
National Curriculum: 1b
Time: During a particular lesson or day
You will need: Pupils' journals
Organization: Pupils make notes in their journals

1. Ask pupils to write down in their journals any mistakes they make during the course of the lesson or the entire day.

2. Ask them to write under their list of mistakes what they believe they have learned as a consequence. Tell the pupils that they will be able to discuss their answers the next day/in the next self-esteem lesson.

3. You could start this discussion (the next day/lesson) by first pairing up the pupils and asking each pair to discuss their notes.

4. Then ask the pairs (or the individual pupils) to share with the whole class what they have discussed. As not all pupils will feel confident to do this in a large group, you might choose to make this optional.

In this section, the learning focus is on pupils gaining an understanding of what values are and exploring the difference between healthy and unhealthy values and how they influence self-esteem.

What Do We Mean by Values?

When we know the things that are important to us – our values – it is easier to deal with people who attempt to impose their own values on us (when those values are not the same as ours).

Values guide our decisions and choices, influence our communication and interactions with others and help determine what we believe is important in our lives. For example, many people value time spent with their family and friends; this value guides them to invest time and energy in this area of priority.

Ignoring our true values often leads to unhealthy self-esteem, because we start experiencing inner conflict and stress. Taking the same example as in the previous paragraph, we find that our time and focus get directed into areas other than being with our friends and family, and the enjoyable times spent together become fewer and fewer. As this is an important aspect of our lives, the result is feelings of frustration, guilt and anger – emotions that have a negative effect on our self-esteem.

Pupil Activity 12

What are My Values?

National Curriculum: 1a, 1b, 4a
Time: 45 minutes
You will need: One copy of 'What are My Values?' (pages 29–30) per pupil
Organization: Individual work and class or pair feedback

1. Pupils work individually, first reading through 'What are My Values?' (page 29), then circling or highlighting the words that *strongly* identify their own values.

2. The pupils then work through the list again, putting a cross beside the words that **do not** reflect their own values.

3. Explain to the pupils that the guideline for their choices is their willingness and motivation to dedicate a significant amount of time and energy to each value, and that the value is something they believe is important to them.

4. Once the pupils have done this, ask them to select five values that are important to them and write these down on the second part of the sheet (page 30). Then ask them to do the same for five items that **do not** reflect their values.

5. The pupils now review these selected values and ask themselves the following questions:
   - Do I spend a large amount of my time and energy on my strongest values?
     or
   - Do I spend my time and focus on the values that I **do not** believe are important?

6. At this point, ask pupils to share their ideas with another pupil. Alternatively, you can have a class discussion, with each pupil sharing one part of this exercise with the other pupils.

7. As a whole class, discuss the reasons why we sometimes lose sight of what we value highly in our lives, spending more time and energy instead on value areas that are not important and perhaps even interfere with our lives. This could include talking about how focusing on unimportant or interfering values contributes to unhealthy self-esteem.

Results of Value Conflict – Unhealthy Self-esteem

Prompts
- Unhappy relationships with friends and/or family
- High levels of stress
- Frustration
- Guilt
- Blaming others
- Emotional confusion

What are My Values?

1. Read through this list of values and circle or highlight those you believe are important values for you. For example, are positive friendships of value to you in your life?

2. Next, read through the list again and put a cross (**X**) beside those values that **do not** reflect your own.

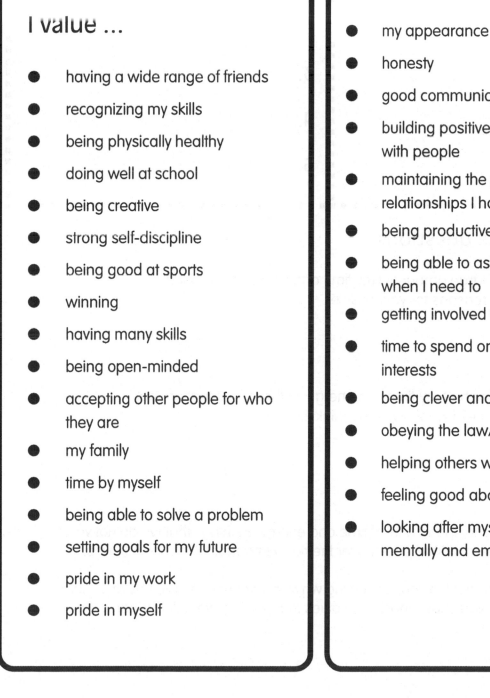

I value ...

- having a wide range of friends
- recognizing my skills
- being physically healthy
- doing well at school
- being creative
- strong self-discipline
- being good at sports
- winning
- having many skills
- being open-minded
- accepting other people for who they are
- my family
- time by myself
- being able to solve a problem
- setting goals for my future
- pride in my work
- pride in myself

- my appearance
- honesty
- good communication with others
- building positive relationships with people
- maintaining the positive relationships I have
- being productive
- being able to ask for help when I need to
- getting involved with school activities
- time to spend on my hobbies/ interests
- being clever and witty
- obeying the law/rules
- helping others when I can
- feeling good about myself
- looking after myself physically, mentally and emotionally

3. In the columns below, write down five important values that you circled on the list and five values you considered not important to you.

Five Things I Value Highly:	Five Things I Don't Value Highly:
1.	1.
2.	2.
3.	3.
4.	4.
5.	5.

Ask yourself these questions:

a) Do I spend a large amount of my time and energy on my highest values? Give reasons for your answer.

b) Do I spend much of my time and energy on the values that are not important to me? Explain why you think this is so.

Note: It is very easy for us to spend a lot of time and energy on things that we do not value highly, and they often seem to take priority over the really important things in our lives.

4. Talk with the person next to you, explaining why/how your five top values are important to you, and then why you chose those five values that you believe reflect what is not important to you.

Healthy and Unhealthy Values
(Recognizing the Difference)

By now your pupils should have a good sense of the differences between healthy and unhealthy self-esteem, but being able to *recognize* the difference between the healthy and unhealthy values underpinning self-esteem is another matter.

Use the points immediately below as prompts for an initial class discussion, and then follow on with the activity, which is designed to help pupils to identify their own healthy and unhealthy values. The class discussion will allow pupils to establish the meanings and differences between the two before they work on their own to consolidate this understanding.

Healthy Values	Unhealthy Values
You have chosen these values for yourself, as important to you.	These encourage you to behave and make choices based on what someone else tells you is the way to behave and choose.
They 'fit' your lifestyle and who you are.	They leave you feeling unsure of who you are, and of what you want.
They help you achieve your goals and get the most out of life.	They make you feel restricted in your choices and limited in the goals you can achieve.
They include language that is inclusive, positive and self-enhancing.	They include language that results in 'all or nothing', 'good or bad', 'right or wrong'; there is no in-between, no room for making mistakes.

Healthy or Unhealthy
National Curriculum: 1a, 1b, 4a
Time: 30 minutes
You will need: One copy of 'Healthy and Unhealthy Values' (page 32) per pupil
Organization: Individual/pair work followed by class feedback

Pupil Activity

13

1. Give the pupils copies of the 'Healthy and Unhealthy Values' sheet (page 32).

2. Ask them to read, either individually or in pairs, through the list of examples, deciding whether their own values are healthy, unhealthy or a mixture of the two. As they have already identified their values in the previous activity, you could suggest that they refer to that list to help them complete this exercise.

3. As a whole class, discuss issues arising from this activity, asking for suggestions and examples of values and how they can be either healthy or unhealthy.

Healthy and Unhealthy Values: What is the Difference?

1. Read through the following points. These will help you decide whether your own values are healthy, unhealthy or a mixture of the two. Tick (✓) the statements that relate to you.

Healthy Values	Unhealthy Values
❏ You have chosen these values as important for you. ❏ These values do not hurt other people. ❏ They are realistic, enabling you to be who you are and who you want to be. ❏ These values involve and continue to encourage good communication with others, such as friends, family and teachers.	❏ Someone else tells you how you should think/feel/behave. ❏ These values intentionally hurt or put other people down. ❏ These values stop you from building positive relationships with other people. ❏ They can include disrespect for others, bullying and uncaring attitudes and behaviours.

Having read through these ideas, in the table below write your own values in the left-hand column and beside each (ie in the right-hand column) whether the value is healthy or unhealthy. Say why you believe this.

My Values	Healthy or Unhealthy? Why?
1.	
2.	
3.	
4.	
5.	

Healthy or Unhealthy

National Curriculum: 1a, 1b, 2c, 4a, 4d
Time: 30 minutes
You will need: One copy of 'Healthy or Unhealthy? You Decide' (page 34) per pupil or pair
Organization: Pair work followed by class feedback

Pupil Activity

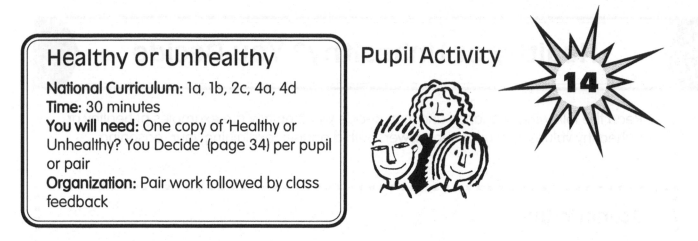

1. Hand out the three scenarios for this activity, 'Healthy or Unhealthy? You Decide' (page 34).
2. In pairs, pupils work through the scenarios to determine whether healthy or unhealthy values are being demonstrated.
3. Discuss each pair's answers and comments as a whole class.

Healthy or Unhealthy? You Decide

1. Read the following scenarios and then decide whether they are examples of healthy or unhealthy values. Discuss your answers with a partner, explaining your reasoning.

Scenario One

It is nearly the end of the maths class when a group of pupils start talking amongst themselves. Suddenly, one of the pupils in this group shouts out to the teacher, telling him that the lesson was 'boring, stupid and a waste of time' and asking why should they bother trying to learn anything if this is the best he can give them. The rest of the group and some of the other class members start laughing.

Questions
1. What do you think of this pupil's behaviour? Do you think it is acceptable? Why or why not?
2. What sort of values are being demonstrated here?
3. What about the values of the rest of the class – what values are they sharing?
4. Where do you think these pupils learned such behaviour?

Scenario Two

Your school is introducing a new, school-wide project aimed at reducing bullying. The project will include all pupils, with the expectation of changing behaviour and attitudes towards bullying. The aim is for everyone to realize how unacceptable this type of behaviour is.

Questions
1. What values does the school see as important?
2. Is this an example of healthy or unhealthy values? Why?

Scenario Three

Three of your friends were late for class today. As a consequence, they are given an after-school detention for half an hour.

Questions
1. Do you think this is a fair school rule?
2. What values is the school demonstrating in taking this action?
3. Is this an example of healthy or unhealthy values? Why?

In this section, pupils will learn about 'self-talk', identifying their own negative messages and creating positive alternatives. The word 'should' can be a powerful negative influence in a person's 'self-talk'. As such, this section continues by helping pupils to recognize any negative 'should' messages and then to create and replace them with positive, self-affirming alternatives.

Eliminating the Negative

Eliminating negative 'self-talk' habits takes practice – on a daily, situation-by-situation basis. The trick is to catch ourselves being negative, in our thoughts and attitudes, so that we can work on changing the messages we give ourselves, thereby creating more positive, healthy communication with ourselves and others.

When considering a positive alternative to a negative message, simple but very effective phrases to start with can include:

- ◆ 'It's OK to ... '
- ◆ 'It's OK if ... '
- ◆ 'It's OK when ... '

A couple of completed examples follow. You could use them with your pupils when you start this lesson.

Negative 'Self-talk' Examples	Positive Alternatives
'I feel really stupid. I can't contribute anything to this conversation.'	'I don't know everything. No one does. It's OK to listen.'
'I can't do this work. It's too difficult. I'm not clever enough.'	'I am still learning this work. It's OK to work at my own pace so that I can understand the material.'

Before you work through the activities with the pupils, think about your own negative statements and identify some positive alternatives. It is much easier to help pupils understand this concept and practise changing their thinking if you can approach the learning from personal experience and knowledge. Here is an exercise to help you:

1. Write about a time when you felt low, sad and unhappy with yourself. What was the situation or event that prompted you to feel this way? If it involved another person, what were they doing that influenced how you were feeling? Now think about your 'self-talk'. What were you telling yourself at this time? Write down the key words or sentences in the left-hand column of the 'Self-image and Language Inventory' table (page 42), just as if you were saying them to yourself.

2. Now think of some times when you experienced a positive situation, a time when you felt happy, satisfied or at peace. Write down on a piece of paper the words or phrases you would use to describe how you felt and what you were thinking at this time. Using these ideas, create some positive alternative 'self-talk' messages for yourself in the right-hand column of the table.

Pupil Activity 15

Changing Negative Self-talking into Positive

National Curriculum: 1a, 1b, 2f, 4a
Time: 45 minutes
You will need: One copy of 'Changing Negative Self-talking to Positive' (page 38) per pupil
Organization: Individual/pair work followed by class feedback

1. Provide pupils with 'Changing Negative 'Self-talk' into Positive' (page 38) and work through the same process with the pupils that you have just done (identifying negative 'self-talk' and changing the language around to make it more positive).
2. Encourage them to work either in pairs or individually to complete this exercise.
3. Ask for ideas, examples or feedback as part of a whole-class discussion.

The Word 'Should'

The word 'should' often creates a negative meaning, whether we use it when talking to other people or talking to ourselves. It is a word that can give the impression of blaming, giving advice when it has not been asked for, imposing a rule on another person's behaviour or imposing rules on our own.

'Shoulds', or rules, start when we are young. We need to learn how to live in the community, and in wider society. As we grow up, we depend on others to help us learn about the world – people like our parents, our teachers and our elders. Gradually, we start recognizing what we think and believe for ourselves, rather than waiting for someone else to tell us. However, some of those earlier rules stay with us, even if we are not conscious of them – these are rules that we learned when we were too young to know that there were other choices (and too young to make such decisions on our own, anyway).

The word 'should' communicates our values and beliefs – our rules for living. For example, some people believe that we should never be unwell and take time off work, but this belief actually sets us up to fail; we can't always avoid being unwell.

Many 'shoulds' (and the rules they denote) are negative. However, some refer to positive, healthy ways of living, seeing ourselves and relating to others. The important thing is to be able to distinguish between the two.

Healthy 'shoulds' follow these principles:

1. They encourage positive behaviour, support positive thinking and promote a positive image of ourselves. For example:
    ✔ 'I should be respectful towards teachers and my parents.'
    ✔ 'I should spend time every day acknowledging my achievements.'

2. They create a feeling of happiness and well-being. For example:
    ✔ 'I should take time out to do something I enjoy, especially when I feel stressed.'

3. They offer rules that 'fit' with our lifestyles, the way we think and the choices we make and feel right about making for ourselves. For example:
    ✔ 'I should learn from others and make decisions for myself based on this learning.'

4. They provide rules that are our own, not someone else's; that is, we don't feel that we have to live a certain way because someone tells us this is the way to live. For example:
    ✔ 'I should be *guided* by my parents' values and *identify* what my own values are. What is important to them may not always be as important to me.'

5. They include language that allows for the human element that we all make mistakes and that it is acceptable to do so. For example:
    ✔ 'I should remember that it's OK to make mistakes.'

6. They encourage us to look after ourselves, be self-supportive and tap into support networks. For example:
    ✔ 'I should take time every day to read through my strengths list.'
    ✔ 'I should spend time with my friends on a regular basis.'

But even with these examples, 'should' has a prescriptive sound to it. Ultimately, the most positive and powerful way of creating a healthy 'should' (rule) is to get rid of the word 'should' altogether. Replace it with a word or phrase that feels and sounds less like a command or demand, such as 'could', 'can', 'need to', 'like to' or 'choose to'.

What you are trying to achieve with your pupils is to facilitate their understanding of how they can change negative 'self-talk' into positive by altering their language and ways of thinking, particularly with regard to 'shoulds'. Giving them healthier options in their thinking and beliefs ultimately influences their self-esteem.

Negative 'Self-talk'	Positive

Healthy or Unhealthy 'Shoulds'

National Curriculum: 1a, 1b, 2b, 2d
Time: 30 minutes
You will need: One large sheet of paper and pens per group
Organization: Small-group work and class feedback

Pupil Activity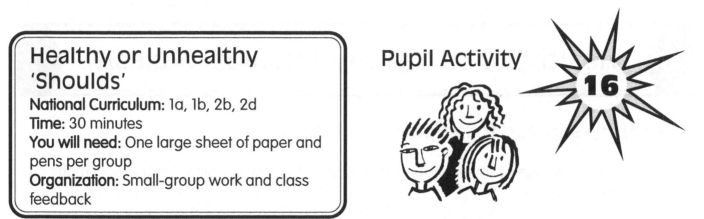

This activity encourages pupils to identify 'should' messages without differentiating between whether they are 'healthy' or 'unhealthy'. Through class discussion, they can decide which are healthy and which are unhealthy.

1. On a large sheet of paper, using felt-tipped pens, pupils work in small groups to create a list of 'should' messages. Ask them to think of messages they can remember from when they were growing up to those they are aware of now. Write some prompts on the board to help them get started.

Prompts
- ☐ I should be seen but not heard.
- ☐ I should do well at school.
- ☐ I should be a good friend.
- ☐ I should always clean my shoes.
- ☐ I should look after my younger sister/brother.
- ☐ I should be happy, and never be angry.

2. Once they have created a list, the members of each group leave their poster in place and move around the room, reading one another's ideas.
3. Generate a whole-class discussion. Ask each group to read out their list, perhaps then adding some new ideas to the prompt list on the board.
4. Continue with the whole-class discussion. Work through the 'should' statements on the board and ask the pupils to decide whether each one is healthy or unhealthy.

Healthy or Unhealthy 'Shoulds'

National Curriculum: 1a, 1b, 2b, 2d
Time: 30 minutes
You will need: One copy of 'Healthy or Unhealthy "Shoulds"?' (page 40) per pupil
Organization: Whole-class work

Pupil Activity

1. Provide pupils with 'Healthy or Unhealthy "Shoulds"?' (page 40), and talk through these.
2. Using the 'should' messages already identified by the pupils and written on the board (*Activity 16*), work as a whole class to rewrite these statements by replacing the word 'should' with the options suggested earlier, that is, 'could', 'choose to' etc. You may decide to use these options or alternative words or phrases.

Note: When you change the statement, you may find it necessary to include the word 'if'. For example, 'I should get more involved in sports activities at school' *might become*, 'I could become more involved in sports *if* I wanted to, but I'm not really that interested.' Or 'I should get top marks at school in all my subjects' *might become* 'I would get top marks *if* I were super-intelligent. I do well in maths and science, and that feels good.'

Healthy or Unhealthy 'Shoulds' (Rules)?

Healthy 'shoulds' follow these principles:

1. They encourage positive behaviour and support a person's positive thinking and image of themselves.

    Examples:
    'I should be respectful toward teachers and my parents.'
    'I should spend time every day acknowledging my achievements.'

2. They create a feeling of happiness.

    Example:
    'I need to take time out to do something I enjoy, especially when I feel stressed.'

3. They provide rules that 'fit' with your lifestyle, the way you think and the choices you make.

    Example:
    'I can learn from others and make decisions for myself based on this learning.'

4. They are rules that are your own, not someone else's; that is, you do not feel you have to live a certain way because someone tells you that this is the way to live.

    Example:
    'I am guided by my parents' values and can also identify what my own values are. What is important to them may not always be as important to me.'

5. They include language that allows for the human element for example, acknowledging that we all make mistakes and it is acceptable to do so.

    Example:
    'It's OK to make mistakes.'

6. They encourage people to look after themselves, support themselves and tap into support networks.

    Examples:
    'I take time every day to read through my strengths list.'
    'I need to spend time with my friends on a regular basis.'

Self-image and Language Inventory

National Curriculum: 1a, 1b
Time: 30 minutes
You will need: One copy of 'Self-image and Language Inventory' (pages 42–43) per pupil
Organization: Individual/pair work and class feedback

Pupil Activity

18

1. Pupils work on their own to complete the 'Self-image and Language Inventory' (pages 42–43).

2. This inventory gives pupils the opportunity to create a description of how they see themselves in relation to the key areas of:
   a) physical appearance
   b) communication with others
   c) personality

3. Ask pupils to repeat this activity, this time working in pairs and discussing aspects of the inventory answers.

4. Create a whole-class discussion that involves transforming pupils' answers to the part 'Influences on My Negative Self-image'.

Transforming Unhealthy 'Shoulds'

National Curriculum: 1a, 1b, 2d, 4a
Time: 30 minutes
You will need: Pupils' journals
Organization: Individual and pair work

Pupil Activity

19

1. Have the pupils work individually to identify and create their own list of 'shoulds' in their journals, getting their ideas from the lists created in the small-groups activity.

2. Working individually or in pairs, each pupil decides which of their 'should' messages are healthy or unhealthy and writes this beside each statement.

3. The pupils then select one or more statements and rewrite them to make healthy statements for themselves that they can copy into their journals.

Self-image and Language Inventory

In the table below, use the headings as a guideline for writing down as many words or phrases that you can think of that *accurately* describe who you are.

Areas to consider	Your description (of yourself)
A. Physical appearance	Example: _ *long legs* _ _ _ _ _ _ _ _ *flat nose* _ _ _ _ _ _ _ *blue eyes* _ _ _ _ _ _ _
B. How I talk to others (Think of friends, family, teachers, club members, other people in the community)	Example: _ *sometimes angry* _ _ _ _ *friendly* _ _ _ _ _ _ _ _ *formal* _ _ _ _ _ _ _ _
C. Personality	Example: _ *friendly* _ _ _ _ _ _ _ _ *shy* _ _ _ _ _ _ _ _ _ *outgoing* _ _ _ _ _ _ _

Now go back through the lists in all three areas and put a plus sign (+) by those words you believe describe your strengths and positive qualities – the things you like about yourself. Put a minus sign (–) beside those words that describe things that you are not happy with.

If you find you have some minuses (negative descriptions of yourself), take a few minutes to think about what has influenced or is influencing these. Write any thoughts you have in the space below.

Influences on My Negative Self-image:

Example:
Things other people say about me.

Discuss your answers with another pupil or wait until the teacher starts a whole-class discussion and contribute your ideas then.

The Power of Language

At this stage, the pupils will have spent some time exploring their 'self-talk' – the language they use to describe themselves, to give themselves messages, etc. Now you want them to explore their choice of language when talking with other people, such as teachers, friends and family members.

Note that this is not just their 'choice of words', but rather 'choice of language'. The language we use in everyday interactions with people has a very strong influence on whether those interactions are positive and healthy. When we talk about our language, it means thinking about and becoming more aware of how we say something, when we say something and the meaning we place on our words, as much as the choice of words themselves. This is a very important point to stress with the pupils as you work through this lesson with them.

Pupil Activity

20

The Power of Language

National Curriculum: 1a, 1b
Time: 50 minutes
You will need: One copy of 'Positive and Negative Language' (page 45) per pupil, board, board pens
Organization: Paired work and class feedback

1. Ask the pupils to complete the 'Positive and Negative Language' exercise (page 45). Encourage them to work in pairs.

2. On completion of the first step of this activity, create a whole-class discussion, asking the pupils to comment on how they decided that some of the words were positive and others were negative. Draw the following table on the board and write up their ideas regarding which language is positive and which negative.

POSITIVE LANGUAGE	NEGATIVE LANGUAGE

3. Continue the discussion, focusing on how positive and negative language influences a person's self-worth, how we all need to be aware of the language we use with others and how it affects the quality and health of our friendships and family relationships. You may choose to pair up pupils again at some point during the discussion, then return to the whole class to continue talking about this topic.

Positive and Negative Language

1. Work through this activity with another pupil. You have 10 minutes to complete it.

2. Read through the following list and consider whether each word has a positive or negative meaning.

3. Use the table below to organize the words into those two categories – 'Positive' and 'Negative'. As you complete this activity, think about how these words influence your self-worth and self-image, and the self-worth of others.

Word List

mistakes	anger	controlling	enthusiastic
failure	jealousy	goal-directed	temperamental
achievement	fair	open	unselfish
successful	friendly	competent	uncaring
happy	dumb	selfish	withdrawn
self-reliant	thoughtless	careless	quiet
hopeless	helpful	unthinking	afraid
average	secure	boring	hopeless
OK	accepting	involved	useless
responsible	power	interesting	aware
lazy	forgetful	different	faults
critical	strength	weak	relaxed
organized	quality	deceptive	respect

Positive Words	Negative Words

Pupil Activity 21

Improving a Negative Self-image
National Curriculum: 1a, 1b, 4a
Time: 60 minutes
You will need: Board, board pens, flip-chart/ large piece of paper and pens per group
Organization: Whole-class introduction and small-group work

1. Once the pupils have completed *Pupil Activity 20*, encourage another whole-class discussion, this time asking them for ideas about what can influence a negative self-image.

2. Write the pupils' ideas on the board and suggest that they copy these down into their journals.

Prompts:
- Lack of self-awareness
- Negative past experiences
- Being around negative people
- Negative 'self-talk'
- Unhappy social environment
- Low self-esteem
- Illness
- Comparing self with others
- Listening to other people's negative language

3. After this brainstorm, split the class into small groups and provide each group with a piece of flip-chart paper and pens. Ask each group to create a mind-map, putting the phrase 'Improving a Negative Self-image' in the middle of the sheet of paper.

4. Each group brainstorms as many ideas as possible about ways to improve a negative self-image.

Prompts
- Changing negative language and negative 'self-talk'
- Ignoring negative comments from others
- Creating a list of our strengths and reading this list every day
- Telling ourselves one positive thing about ourselves every day
- Listening to positive people
- Asking someone we trust to describe our positive qualities

5. Once all groups have a few ideas on their mind-map, ask a spokesperson from each group to present the ideas to the rest of the class.

Note: You could place the mind-maps on the classroom wall for a period of time or put them on the wall each time the class has a self-esteem lesson.

The Language We Use with Others

Pupil Activity

National Curriculum: 1a, 1b, 2c, 4a, 4d
Time: 30 minutes
You will need: One copy of 'The Language We Use with Others' (page 48) per pair or pupil
Organization: Paired work and whole-class feedback

Because the pupils have already completed two activities that focus on looking at themselves, this activity aims to encourage thinking about how their language and behaviour can influence someone else's self-image.

1.   Direct the pupils to read through the scenario given in 'The Language We Use with Others' (page 48) and to work in pairs to answer the questions. This handout provides just one example that can prompt pupils to think about how their self-image can be affected negatively by language. You may have a more relevant scenario to use.

2.   Once the pair-work part of this activity is finished, create a whole-class discussion to conclude the activity, asking for pupils' ideas and answers and any general thoughts about this topic.

The Language We Use with Others

1. Read through the scenario below and then work in pairs to discuss what you think is 'unhealthy' about it. Remember that 'unhealthy' means things that are negative, either in terms of how we feel about ourselves or what we do to other people to create unhealthiness in relationships.

2. Think about the language being used, the quality of the relationship and other communication skills that are being used/not being used effectively.

3. At the end of the scenario, there are some questions for you to discuss with your partner. A whole-class discussion will follow this activity. You can offer your ideas to the rest of the group then.

Friends or Not?

Sue: 'So, what do you think of Leanne's new haircut? I think it looks so "last year"!'

Adrienne: 'Yeah, I'd be really embarrassed if I had to come to school looking like that.'

Sue: 'Still, she doesn't do much to help herself anyway, regardless of her horrible haircut. I mean, look at her face – all that acne – and she always looks so unclean. Yuck. I reckon she smells too. I try not to sit next to her in class.'

Adrienne: (laughing) 'Did you hear her in class this morning? Talk about stupid. She was asking such dumb questions that anybody else would know. Is she thick or what?'

Sue: 'I reckon. No wonder she doesn't have any friends. Who would want to be seen with her? Not me, that's for sure.'

Adrienne: 'Thank goodness we're not like her. Oops, look out, here she comes now. Let's go before she gets too near us. Don't want to be seen with her.'

Questions:

a) If Leanne had overheard this whole conversation, how do you think she would be feeling?

b) What language were Sue and Adrienne using that would influence Leanne's negative self-image? Write the words down in the space below.

c) What other behaviour were Sue and Adrienne engaging in that would easily affect Leanne negatively (eg. staring at her, whispering …)?

d) What feelings and behaviour are Sue and Adrienne encouraging in each other?

The activities in this section will enable pupils to recognize those things that can 'trample' self-esteem; these activities can also help pupils defend themselves against negativity by helping them to access their support networks. Activities include pupils exploring pressures or problems they are experiencing in their lives (inside and outside school) and identifying support people or systems that could help reduce such pressures. They will explore different kinds of support networks and identify how they can give themselves support.

The Importance of Support

We are surrounded by people every day, whether at school, at home or in the community we live in. Not everyone will necessarily provide us with support when we need it, therefore it is important for us not only to know who will support us, but also to learn how to give ourselves support.

Support can come in many different shapes and forms. It may be from other people, it may be through our involvement with a sporting activity or hobby and it may even come from ourselves – positive 'self-talk', acknowledging our achievements, setting goals and so on. A support network of other people is vital in helping us to maintain healthy self-esteem.

As you have been discussing with your pupils throughout these sessions, it can sometimes be very difficult for us to maintain any feelings of self-worth and 'OK-ness', as much as we may try to. So, instead of dreading these times, a better idea Is first to identify what may be causing these feelings of unhealthy self-esteem (a topic explored in the sections covered so far in this resource book) and, second, to identify the supports that we need. Sometimes, we feel we can't 'impose' on other people. But that is not relevant in relation to a support network. 'Support people' are there because they are happy and willing to talk things through, help as required, assist with problem-solving and sometimes just to be there.

Pupil Activity 23

Support Networks

National Curriculum: 1a, 1b, 2h, 3f, 4a, 4g
Time: 65 minutes
You will need: Board, board pen, one copy of 'Support Networks' (page 51) per pupil and 'How to Give Yourself Support' (page 52) per pupil
Organization: Class and individual work

Note: Read and use the information contained in 'How to Give Yourself Support' (page 52) as an added prompt to help with the activities below before giving this handout to the pupils (see part 5 of this activity).

1. Create a class brainstorm. Write the term 'Support Networks' on the board and ask pupils to contribute their ideas of the possible networks people can have.

   > **Prompts**
   > - Family
   > - Religious institutions
   > - Teachers
   > - Sports clubs
   > - Friends
   > - Hobbies

2. Provide pupils with the 'Support Networks' chart (page 51) and ask them to fill in the support networks they have and feel are important for them, using the list generated from the brainstorm as prompts.

3. As a whole-class exercise, introduce the concept of 'self-support' as an additional tool for pupils to use, that is, how people can support themselves to maintain and build self-esteem in times of stress etc. Write the pupils' ideas on the board.

   > **Prompts**
   > - Setting goals
   > - Celebrating successes
   > - Talking to another person (who is trusted)
   > - Getting adequate sleep

4. During this discussion, incorporate a brainstorm of ideas as to how people can increase their support networks.

   > **Prompts**
   > - Join a club with a friend
   > - Get involved in school activities
   > - Tell someone important in their life about their successes
   > - Start a 'self-achievement' list
   > - Learn to acknowledge what they do well

5. Now provide pupils with the 'How to Give Yourself Support' handout (page 52), and ask them to read through the list of ideas, adding any of their own at the bottom of the page.

Support Networks

In developing your awareness and acceptance of change, it is important not to bottle things up. Talk about things with others.

In the table below, write down the people you may be able to use in your support network.

Support People

eg. close friend

- _____
- _____
- _____
- _____
- _____
- _____
- _____
- _____
- _____
- _____
- _____
- _____

How to Give Yourself Support

- ◆ Listen to and accept positive feedback from other people.
- ◆ Remind yourself of your strengths and abilities – on a daily basis.
- ◆ Don't forget to use your support network when you need to.
- ◆ Create some short- and long-term goals for yourself and check these on a regular basis, to track the progress you are making.
- ◆ When you create your goals, make sure they are realistic and achievable. Identify the things you really want to achieve.
- ◆ Sometimes it helps to write down how you are feeling. If you are anxious or worried about something, writing this down can help clarify what is causing this.
- ◆ Make sure you spend time with your friends and talk to them.
- ◆ Keep a balance in your life. Focus your time and energy on your family, your friends, your health and your social needs.
- ◆ Get plenty of sleep.
- ◆ Talk to a professional person if you feel that no one close to you will understand how you are feeling – the school counsellor or your teacher, perhaps.
- ◆ Be nice to yourself. Give yourself a treat sometimes, like buying an ice cream, going for a swim, listening to music etc.
- ◆ Spend time doing things you really enjoy.
- ◆ Believe in who you are, especially now that you have discovered your positive qualities!

Add your own ideas here:

- _____
- _____
- _____
- _____

- _____
- _____
- _____
- _____

Problems/Pressures and Support

National Curriculum: 1a, 1b, 2h, 3f, 4a, 4g
Time: 30 minutes
You will need: One copy of 'Problems/Pressures and Support' (page 54) per pupil
Organization: Individual work

This activity helps pupils to identify the things that can affect how people feel and how they see themselves, and at the same time identify and acknowledge the strength of support networks and self-support to combat these negative times and influences.

1. Hand out the 'Problems/Pressures and Support' sheet (page 54) for pupils to complete. Explain how the top half of the paper represents any 'pressures' they have in their lives and the bottom half the 'support systems' available to them. Emphasize that the supports include other people and self-support.

2. Continue explaining the activity, suggesting that pupils think about things in their life that they feel cause them stress, things that negatively influence their self-esteem (the 'pressures'). Ask them to identify which are the biggest pressures and to place these near the 'me' symbol in the middle of the sheet. Pressures that are not so large, but still have the potential to negatively influence their self-esteem, should be placed farthest from the 'me' symbol. Thus, the more distant the pressure is from the 'me' symbol, the less impact it has on their self-esteem.

3. Repeat this process, this time identifying support systems. Ask the pupils to identify what things or people (or self) give them the most support when they need it and to place these close to the 'me' symbol. They then need to determine what other support systems exist that still provide them with support but are not as strong. These should be placed farthest from the 'me' symbol.

Anchor

National Curriculum: 1a, 1b, 3f, 4a, 4g
Time: 20 minutes
You will need: One copy of 'Anchor' (page 55) per pupil
Organization: Individual work

1. Provide pupils with the picture of the 'Anchor' (page 55). Explain to them that 'anchors' provide support and stability by keeping objects in a secure place, and that the purpose of the activity is for them to identify those things that provide such stability and security – *support* – in their lives.

2. Working individually, each pupil writes down, around the anchor picture, their achievements, goals, successes, things they like doing, people they enjoy spending time with etc.

3. Suggest to the pupils that they pin their list up on their wall at home, or keep it where they will see it every day, to remind themselves of all the positive things in their life that provide 'anchors'.

Problems/Pressures

ME

Support

Anchor

Pupil Activity

26

Other Sources of Support
National Curriculum: 4g
Time: 15 minutes
You will need: Board, board pen
Organization: Class discussion

Conduct a general class discussion and brainstorm, identifying more 'formal' services that can also provide support.

Prompts
◆ Counsellor
◆ Form teacher
◆ Careers services
◆ Doctor

The 'OK Zone'/The 'Learning Zone'

We all have situations and events in which we feel comfortable and relaxed (adults and children alike) – our 'OK zone'. Then, there are times when we feel very uncomfortable and not at all sure of ourselves – this we call the 'learning zone'. Giving this zone the title 'learning' helps us to relate our uncomfortable feelings to something meaningful and positive.

We all have to move out of our 'OK zone' at times, whether by our own choosing or not. When we do, we start to learn about our responses to new situations as well as new ways of dealing or coping with such times. The aim of this section is to discover how we can best deal with this new learning, and how to look after ourselves (our self-esteem) in the process.

Some people welcome challenges and enjoy taking risks in order to experience a new expectation or demand of themselves. Some people don't! Even if you are not a risk-taker, the more you can accept that new learning (ie moving from your 'OK zone' to your 'learning zone') is a part of life, the easier you will find it to adapt to new situations, cope with frightening events and keep your confidence and self-esteem intact.

Before taking the pupils through this section of learning, complete your own 'OK' and 'Learning' zones diagram (page 58). Then use this activity with the pupils.

Defining 'OK' and 'Learning' Zones

National Curriculum: 1a, 1b, 1c, 4a
Time: 45 minutes
You will need: Board, board pen, one copy of 'OK' and 'Learning' Zone per pupil
Organization: Whole-class introduction and feedback, and individual/pair work

Pupil Activity

27

1. Having worked through the 'OK' and 'Learning' Zones diagram (page 58) yourself, give this activity to the pupils to complete. You may need to spend some time before they begin work on it, as a whole class, brainstorming the definitions of 'OK' and 'learning' zones, and giving an example of each to encourage the pupils to think about their own 'zones'.

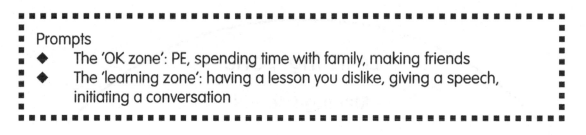

> Prompts
> ◆ The 'OK zone': PE, spending time with family, making friends
> ◆ The 'learning zone': having a lesson you dislike, giving a speech, initiating a conversation

2. Ask the pupils to work on their own diagram initially and then to discuss some of their ideas with a partner.

3. Return to a whole-class discussion. Talk through how to move from the 'OK zone' to the 'learning zone', highlighting this as an important part of the learning in this activity.

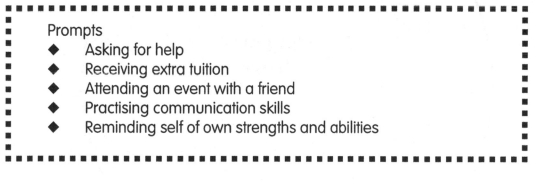

> Prompts
> ◆ Asking for help
> ◆ Receiving extra tuition
> ◆ Attending an event with a friend
> ◆ Practising communication skills
> ◆ Reminding self of own strengths and abilities

'OK' and 'Learning' Zones

1. The diagram below is for you to fill in using the following guidelines. You will have a good idea of what the terms 'OK zone' and 'learning zone' mean from discussions with your teacher. So, take some time to think about those events, situations, people and/or activities that you consider belong in your 'OK zone'. Think about past and present experiences. Then, do the same for your 'learning zone'. An example for each 'zone' has been provided to get you started.

2. When you have done this, discuss your ideas with another pupil.

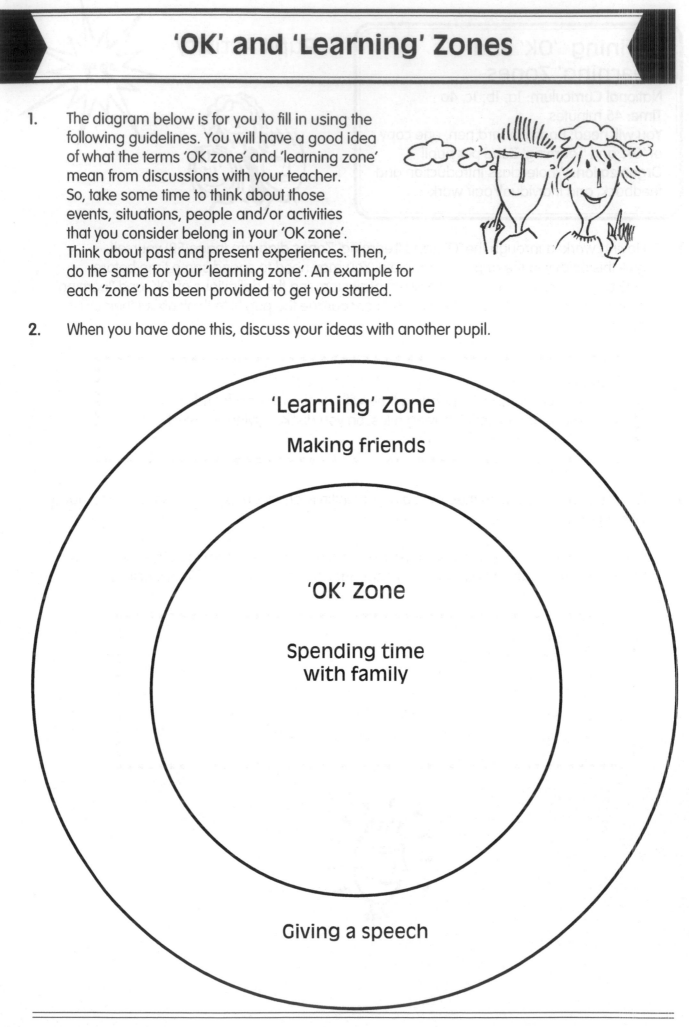

'Learning' Zone

Making friends

'OK' Zone

Spending time
with family

Giving a speech

Building and maintaining healthy self-esteem is an ongoing activity and a vital one – something we have to work on every day. Even though we can get support from other people, it is important that we look after ourselves. As the previous sections have emphasized, self-support involves positive thinking, recognizing our values, identifying our strengths and attributes, changing our negative self-talk and taking every opportunity to 'catch' ourselves feeling good and confident. We can do these things at any time of the day, in any situation we are involved in.

For pupils, this awareness can be related to inside and outside school hours. Self-esteem awareness goes well beyond classroom self-esteem sessions.

Opportunities to Maintain Healthy Self-esteem

National Curriculum: 1a, 1b, 4a
Time: 30 minutes
You will need: Pens and flip-chart/large piece of paper per group, one copy of 'Opportunities to Maintain Healthy Self-esteem' (page 61) per pupil
Organization: Small-group work and class feedback

Pupil Activity

28

This activity aims to encompass much of the learning that has already occurred in this project, serving as a summary of sorts. It requires directing your pupils to think again about the different strategies they can use to look after themselves and maintain healthy self-esteem.

1. Pupils work in small groups. Provide each group with flip-chart paper and pens, and ask them to write the words 'Opportunities to Maintain Healthy Self-esteem' (page 61) at the top of their piece of paper. The purpose of this part of the activity is for pupils to identify opportunities available to them inside and outside school to build healthy self-esteem and to change unhealthy self-esteem habits, such as negative 'self-talk'.

2. Ask each group to share their ideas with the rest of the class.

3. Now provide each pupil with 'Opportunities to Maintain Healthy Self-esteem' (page 61). Working individually, pupils determine which of the discussed opportunities relate specifically to their lives, and also fill in their own ideas.

Pupil Activity 29

The Self-esteem Card Game

National Curriculum: 1a, 1b, 1c, 4a, 4g
Time: 20–30 minutes
You will need: One set of cards (pages 63–64) photocopied and cut out (possibly laminated) per pair
Organization: Pairwork

This is a fun activity that you can use with your pupils at any time during the project.

1. Organize the pupils to work in pairs and provide each pair with a set of cards.

2. Each pair selects one card at a time and works through the activity written on that card.

3. You may choose to finish the card game with a whole-class discussion, asking the pupils to comment on any of the card-related activities they worked through.

Note: Use page 62 as a backing for the cards.

Opportunities to Maintain Healthy Self-esteem

Opportunities during school-time

Examples:
- Congratulate self
- Ask for help
- Recognize when you are feeling good

Your Turn
- _____
- _____
- _____
- _____

- _____
- _____
- _____
- _____

Opportunities outside school-time

Examples:
- Celebrate achievement of personal goals
- Spend quality time with family/friends
- Join a club

Your Turn
- _____
- _____
- _____
- _____

- _____
- _____
- _____
- _____

The
Self-esteem
Card Game

The
Self-esteem
Card Game

The
Self-esteem
Card Game

The
Self-esteem
Card Game

The
Self-esteem
Card Game

The
Self-esteem
Card Game

The
Self-esteem
Card Game

The
Self-esteem
Card Game

Write down three personal qualities that describe you in a positive way.

Describe these qualities by noting:

1. How they developed
2. How you maintain them
3. How you recognize them
4. The positive consequences

Write down a time when you felt good about yourself.

Describe the situation or event and explain how you felt.

Share one of your personal strengths with another person, and ask them to share one of their own.

Write down one thing you would really like to do in your life, then turn this into a goal statement, identifying the future steps you will need to take to achieve it.

Dreams can become reality
What are your dreams?
Identify some of your dreams (the things you would like to happen), then think about the things that stop you from following your dreams.

How are you stopping yourself from achieving your dreams?

What actions do you need to take to start achieving your dreams?

Write down a time when you achieved a goal you had set yourself.

Note what you did, the strengths you used and the actions you took.

Divide a page into two columns. In the left-hand column, write down as many negative words as you can think of, particularly words that people (yourself included) tend to use to describe themselves.

Now, in the right-hand column, find a positive word or phrase that replaces each negative one.

Draw a circle in the middle of a piece of paper. Place your name in the middle (or a picture of yourself), then identify those people you see as support systems for you.

These may include members of groups, clubs etc.

Identify one of your achievements and decide how you can congratulate yourself for it.

Carry out what you decide.

Make a list of all your achievements and write down how you will congratulate yourself for each.

Be a little creative and think of a series of different ways.

List those support networks that provide you with guidance and a willingness to help.

Hint: Someone who listens is often one of our strongest support systems.

Identify two goals for yourself, focusing on the areas in your life that you would like to change, improve or develop.

Write them in a journal, or somewhere where you can review them whenever you need to.

Start a conversation with someone, giving them some information about yourself. Talk only in positive terms and stop your dialogue whenever you hear yourself using negative language.

Hint: Talk about your background, upbringing, family, work, health, social network, achievements and values.

Divide a large sheet of paper into two columns. Title the left-hand column 'NOW' and the right-hand column 'FUTURE'.

Describe your present situation, including stage of personal growth, then illustrate where you would like to be in the future, using words, symbols or pictures.

Create a list of your personal strengths and qualities. Select one and think back to a past situation when you used that strength.

Share this example with another person, then work through your list and repeat the same exercise with each strength.

Start a journal, noting in it all the achievements that you are making, both small and large.

Start it now by jotting down all the things you have accomplished today; since yesterday; and over the last week.

Make this a daily activity.

Setting Goals

A good way to start thinking about learning related to self-esteem is to think about and set some goals in relation to what you want to achieve by the end of this project (these are your *short-term goals*). At the end of the project, you can identify some larger goals that highlight any changes you want to make, particularly in relation to your level of self-confidence and self-esteem.

People usually have a combination of short- and long-term goals.

Goals:

 enable you to focus on where you want to be in life.

 identify what you want to achieve.

 identify the steps to take to help you reach those future dreams.

As your teacher discusses the self-esteem project with you, he or she will talk through the different topics that will be included in the project sessions. As you listen, start setting some short-term goals for yourself. Ask, 'What would I like to achieve by the end of the project?' Your answer might be, for example:

❒ Understand the meaning of self-esteem and identify my own level of self-esteem.

❒ Be able to identify how to keep friendships positive.

❒ Communicate better with my teachers and my family.

Use the 'Goal Sheet – Short-term Goals' on the next page to start writing down some of your own short-term goals. You will receive another goal sheet at the end of the project. Use this to identify and write down your long-term goals.

Goal Sheet – Short-term Goals

Step One:

◆ Decide what your goals are. Try to identify at least two.

◆ It may help to start your goal statement with something like:

'By the end of this project, I will/I want to ... '

Goal One: _____

Goal Two: _____

Goal Three: _____

Goal Four: _____

Step Two:

◆ Now decide if your goals are realistic. Ask:

'Will I be able to achieve these goals by the end of the project?'

'Do I have the resources to help me achieve these goals?'

'Do I believe I have the ability and motivation to reach these goals?'

Are my goals realistic?   YES   NO   (circle one)

If NO, how can I rewrite them?

Rewrite:

_____

_____

_____

Short-term Goals (continued)

Step Three:

◆ What resources or support will you need to help you achieve your goals?

◆ Resources/support I will need (tick any you agree with):

☐ Friends to talk to

☐ Family encouragement

☐ Help from the teacher

☐ Opportunities to practise the skills

☐ Time to think through the material

Other suggestions:

_____

_____

_____

Step Four:

◆ You now need to consider what obstacles might get in the way of you achieving your goals.

◆ Read through the following list and tick/highlight those things that you think could be obstacles:

☐ *Lack of planning*

☐ *Still unclear about how to achieve goals*

☐ *Too scared to ask for help when I don't understand*

☐ *Lack of support from others*

☐ *Low self-motivation*

Short-term Goals (continued)

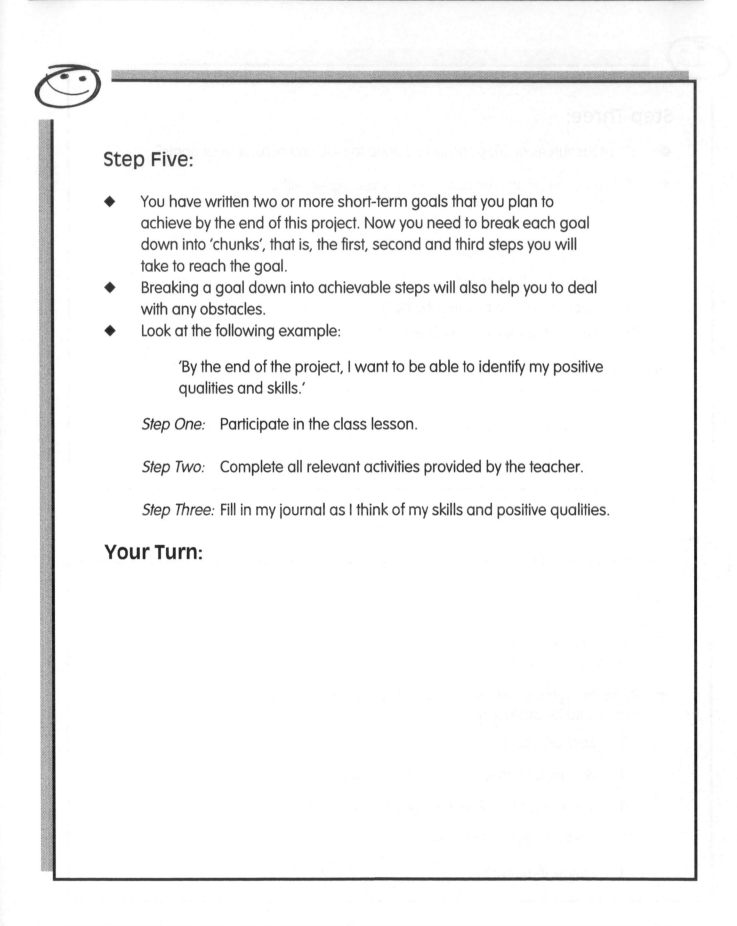

Step Five:

◆ You have written two or more short-term goals that you plan to achieve by the end of this project. Now you need to break each goal down into 'chunks', that is, the first, second and third steps you will take to reach the goal.

◆ Breaking a goal down into achievable steps will also help you to deal with any obstacles.

◆ Look at the following example:

'By the end of the project, I want to be able to identify my positive qualities and skills.'

Step One: Participate in the class lesson.

Step Two: Complete all relevant activities provided by the teacher.

Step Three: Fill in my journal as I think of my skills and positive qualities.

Your Turn:

Goal Sheet – Long-term Goals

Question: What would be one important self-esteem area you could develop and continue building on in the future, both at school and in your home life?

Step One:

◆ Decide what your goals are. Try to identify at least two.

◆ It may help to start your goal statement with something like:

'By the end of this project, I will/I want to ... '

Goal One: _____

Goal Two: _____

Goal Three: _____

Goal Four: _____

Step Two:

◆ Now decide if your goals are realistic. Ask:

'Will I be able to achieve these goals within a reasonable period of time?'

'Do I have the resources to help me achieve these goals?'

'Do I believe I have the ability and motivation to reach these goals?'

Are my goals realistic?   YES   NO   (circle one)

If NO, how can I rewrite them?

Rewrite:

_ _

_ _

_ _

Long-term Goals (continued)

Step Three:

◆ What resources or support will you need to help you achieve your goals?

◆ Resources/support I will need (tick any you agree with):

☐ Friends to talk to
☐ Family encouragement
☐ Help from the teacher
☐ Opportunities to practise the skills
☐ Time to think through the material

Other suggestions:

_____

_____

_____

Step Four:

◆ You now need to consider what obstacles might get in the way of you achieving your goals.

◆ Read through the following list and tick/highlight those things that you think could be obstacles:

☐ *Lack of planning*

☐ *Still unclear about how to achieve goals*

☐ *Too scared to ask for help when I don't understand*

☐ *Lack of support from others*

☐ *Low self-motivation*

Long-term Goals (continued)

Step Five:

- ◆ You have written two or more long-term goals that you plan to achieve by the end of this project. Now you need to break each goal down into 'chunks', that is, the first, second and third steps you will take to reach the goal.
- ◆ Breaking a goal down into achievable steps will also help you to deal with any obstacles.
- ◆ Look at the following example:

'After the project, I want to be able to identify my positive qualities and skills.'

Step One: Participate in the class lesson.

Step Two: Complete all relevant activities provided by the teacher.

Step Three: Fill in my journal as I think of my skills and positive qualities.

Your Turn:

Remember: The more you talk to others about what you plan to achieve for yourself and discover their ideas, the more information you will have for further goals and skill development.

Self-evaluation

Checking my goal achievement

Now that you have finished the self-esteem project, it is time to look back through the learning sessions and think about how you have done – what you have achieved, what you have learned about yourself and others and where to go from here.

Read through the following questions, and then answer them thoughtfully and honestly. After you have done that, go to the activity 'Goal Sheets: Long-term Goals' and work through the steps.

1. What are the main things you believe you have learned about your self-esteem?

    Example: Self-esteem influences how I talk to other people.

    Your Turn:

2. What skills have you developed during the project? (Choose as many of the following as you like.)

    ☐ positive thinking   ☐ self-worth

    ☐ being honest with myself   ☐ good communication with others

    ☐ asking for help   ☐ respect for myself

    ☐ respect for other people   ☐ problem-solving

    ☐ setting goals for myself   ☐ expressing my feelings

    ☐ self-responsibility   ☐ establishing support networks

    ☐ supporting myself   ☐ making decisions for myself

    ☐ handling negative comments
        from others well

Checking my goal achievement

3. How much do you think you have changed in a positive way since the project began (circle one)?

   A LOT   QUITE A LOT   SOME   NOT MUCH

4. Write down how you have changed during the project since it started.

   Changes I have made:

5. What is one thing you think you could still improve in?

   Examples: Be more positive in my self-talk.
                   Build better support systems.

   Your turn:

6. Did you achieve the short-term goals you set yourself at the beginning of this project? Answer YES or NO in relation to each one. If NO, what were the obstacles that stopped you?

Lightning Source UK Ltd.
Milton Keynes UK
UKOW07f2253260517

302128UK00002B/18/P